# Down the lughole

# Fiona

Fiona Murphy lives in Weymouth, Dorset with her husband and two grown up children, cat Macey and dog Roxy. Writing stories and poetry was her favourite thing to do at school.

# Michelle

Michelle Last lives in Leicester, England. Ever since she can remember she has enjoyed drawing. She also enjoys reading, drinking tea and one day would love to own a cat.

# Down the Plughole

## a collection of children's poems

### by Fiona Murphy
### and Michelle Last

poetryspace

**Down the Plughole**

First published in Great Britain in 2012 by Poetry Space Ltd

Poetry Space Ltd Company No 7144469

Registered office: 21Davis Close, Barrs Court, Bristol BS30 7BU

www.poetryspace.co.uk

Printed and bound in Great Britain
by Whitehall Printing Company Ltd, Bristol

ISBN 978-0-9565328-8-6

To my children Jordan and Declan.

To Richard , Mum and Dad, thanks for your continuing support.

To Carl, Vicky, Albie and Henry who inspired me and Michelle Last for bringing my poems to life.

Fiona


To Rich, for always being there for me.

To my friends and family, for your support.

And especially to Fiona, without you I would never have gone Down the Plughole...

Michelle

# Contents

Ducks in Trouble 9

Curls 10

A Dragon's Song 13

High in the Sky 14

Pirates Don't Cry 17

School Time 19

Dinosaur Ailments 20

Brotherly Love 23

Sisterly Sharing     24

Shopping with Mum     26

Socks Have Feelings Too     28

Toddlers Tales     31

Rockets Rule     33

Halloween Party     35

Why Mum?     37

Jungle Dreams     38

# DUCKS IN TROUBLE

I am stuck here in a puddle
Standing on one leg!
Not sure where my nest is
Or if I can lay an egg?

# CURLS

Why have I got curly hair?
I want it straight, it's just not fair.

Plaits are the best
with ribbons on the end
but mine curl up
and drive me round the bend.

When I try to brush my hair,
it hurts a lot,
because it's wild
and full of knots.

Mum said "don't worry
you'll love it one day.
When other girls, want it curly
they will have to pay!"

# A DRAGON'S SONG

Down the plughole,
under the bath
there lives a dragon
who is very daft.

His name is Horace,
we don't know where he's from
but when the water goes
he sings his song:

"Gurgle, Gurgle,
Slurrrp, Slurrrp,
Glug, Glug
and a great BIG BURRRRP!"

Now you know
when you hear
that noise,
it's Horace Singing
to all the girls and boys.

# HIGH IN THE SKY

What is your name?
said the Cloud to the Moon.
The man in the Moon laughed,
I have no name
but I can change the tide.
What can you do?

I can change shape, said the cloud
like this, a castle or a dragon.
How clever, said the moon
now blow away, I have work
to do, he said
See you soon, yelled the cloud

changing shape again.

# PIRATES DON'T CRY

Poppy the pirate wanted to be like the
boys,
with a dagger and sword
shouting battle cries.

She did not like pink or anything fluffy.
She liked fighting, mud and
getting mucky.

But one day she got carried away
with her Pirate fun,
tying up her teacher
and demanding a ransom.

So Mum and Dad banned her
pirate disguise,
but Poppy just shrugged
as no pirate cries.

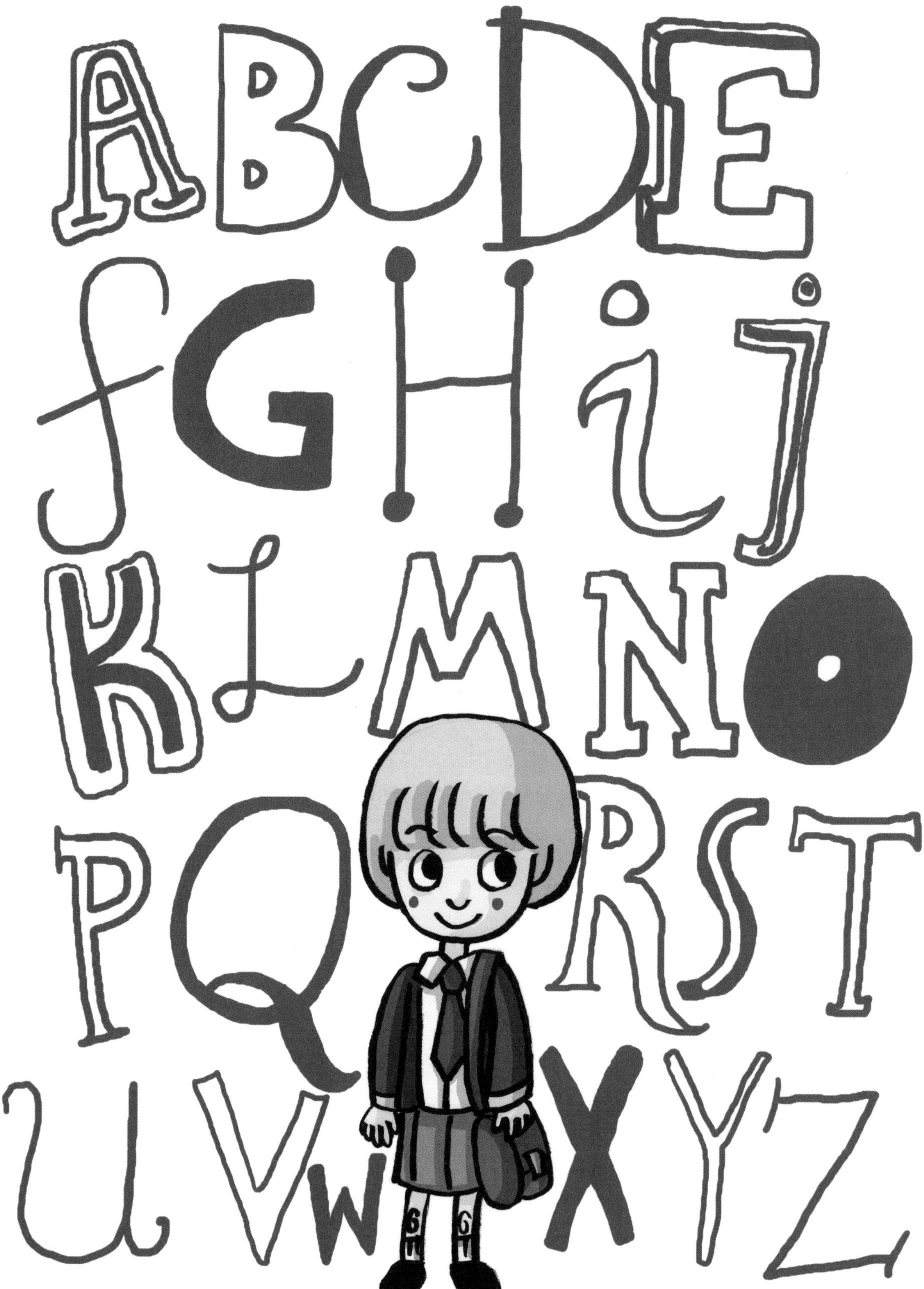
ABCDE
fGHij
KLMNO
PQRST
UVWXYZ

# SCHOOL TIME

Now I'm nearly five,
 I can go to school.
I must learn to read and write
 and follow the rules
I wear my uniform,
 with all my pride.
Hair brushed neatly,
 lunchbox by my side.

Assembly's in the morning,
three playtimes through the day.
'Schooldays are the best'!
is what my mum says.
Now we have learnt our alphabet,
from a to z
it's time for home,
 tea, bath, and then bed.
                    Zzzzzzz.

# DINOSAUR AILMENTS

Sarasauras was covered in spots
and had to stay in bed.

The spots were all over her feet,
her body and on her scaly head.

"It's only chickenpox"! she said,
trying not to scratch.

But her friends all stayed away
as it was easy for dinosaurs, to catch.

# BROTHERLY LOVE

My little brother
is very nearly two
He's always in trouble,
believe me it's true
I keep an eye on him
for my mum,
whilst we wait
for our tea to come.

He's broken our T.V.
and our washing machine
He's always grubby
and never ever clean
Sometimes I shout at him
to "Go Away" !
But I'm really glad
he's here to stay.

# SISTERLY SHARING

My big sister is 4 and a half
she does roly- polys and makes me laugh.

We play together and share our toys,
banging, crashing making lots of noise.

She gets things for me I can't reach
helps me build sandcastles on the beach

She's bigger than me, but I want to know
will I catch her up if I grow?

# SHOPPING WITH MUM

Beware all shoppers who like to stare
There's a manic mother coming
with a pushchair.

She will not stop until she's done
because shopping is
no longer fun.

Gritting her teeth she queues to pay
but her toddler's got loose
and gone astray.

Where can he be? Oh no she shrieks!
He's filling up his pocket
with lots of sweets.

Once more she queues,
but people still stare,
she's got cereal in her hair.
Packing the shopping with a smile on her face
thinking now she can escape this horrid place.

## SOCKS HAVE FEELINGS TOO

I am a lonely sock
left on the stair
I wonder if anyone
even knows I'm there?

I want to be paired
with my sock brother,
I don't look right
if I'm put with another.

So please don't pass me by!
Please pick me up
and have a try
to find my twin
of who I am fond.

We have an incredible
woollen bond!

# TODDLERS TALES

I am the snot monster
walking towards you,
arms outstretched trying to cling on!
Watch out! I don't hang around for very
long.

Stumbling from place to place
Like a spaceman in outer space.
Leaving a trail of destruction behind,
sticky handprints everywhere,
just to remind you I'm there.

With just one smile, a cheesy grin
the monster now hides, deep down within

MA MA, DA DA, I babble away,
this is a toddler's life every day.

# ROCKETS RULE

Floating
in space
with not a care
in the world.
Here is Henry
seven years old.

He's built his rocket
out of cardboard,
tape and plastic.
His view of earth
is simply fantastic.

Now it's time to return
back home to bed.

This spaceman needs

to rest his weary head.

# HALLOWEEN PARTY

Lola loved Halloween
and the hocus pocus fun
as she was a witch just like her mum.

Her dad taught her
his best wizard spells
and she swore an oath never to tell.

Swooping down quickly,
on her old battered broomstick
to the school Halloween party,
with black cat Pickwick.

Lola won the prize
for the best fancy dress.
She was a real witch
and no one guessed.

# WHY MUM?

Why Mum is the sky Blue?
Did God paint it, is it true?

Where does the sun go at night?
Why is the moon shining so bright?

Why do the clouds cry, when it rains?
Have they been told off again?

I don't like the thunder
or the lightning
Why does it have to be
so very frightening?

And Mum, MUM, why is the sky,
always there and so very high?

# JUNGLE DREAMS

Jordan in the jungle, swinging through
the trees
wearing nothing but a couple of leaves.

She spies a lion licking his lips,
he's hoping that she might just slip.

She comes to a river and swims across
showing the crocodiles she's the boss.

The monkeys come to meet her, they
want to play,
throwing coconuts is the game today.
Off once more, she waves goodbye

which way now should she try?
But wait, what's that noise
someone's calling

WAKE UP SLEEPYHEAD

IT'S THE MORNING!